581

Plants That Heal

Plants That Heal

By MILLICENT E. SELSAM

Illustrated by Kathleen Elgin

WILLIAM MORROW AND COMPANY

LIBRARY EDITION 1968

RESPONSIVE ENVIRONMENTS CORP.

Englewood Cliffs, N.J. 07632

The author acknowledges with gratitude the expert advice of Mr. Edson F. Woodward of S. B. Penick and Company.

Library of Congress Catolog Card No. 59-5513.

· · · · · · ·

CONTENTS

Plants That Heal

CHAPTER 1

The Medicine Man and His Herbs

THE plant kingdom was man's only drugstore for countless centuries. If you enter a modern drugstore today, you can hardly find a sign of the use of plants in medicine. But in drugstores fifty years ago the druggist was still measuring quantities of dried leaves, roots, and powders made from plants, and mixing them together into prescriptions. There you actually saw the plants being turned into drugs. Today the number of plants used in medicine has decreased, but hidden away in many pills, capsules, and medicine bottles are the active chemicals originally found in the plant kingdom.

This is because the plants in our fields and forests are amazing chemical factories. They carry out the kind of chemical work for which we need huge boilers, pressure cookers, and other complicated equipment. The carbohydrates, fats, and proteins they manufacture are the plant products we know best. The plants manufacture these from the carbon dioxide of the air plus the water and minerals of the soil, and store them away in roots, stems, leaves, and seeds. We eat hundreds of plants that have such stored-away food. But some plants make other highly complicated chemical substances. These, too, are stored in various parts of the plant. These chemicals may be poisonous, or they may be chemicals that are extremely valuable to us as medicines.

During the many thousands of years that man has been on the earth, he has tried out the plants that grew around him. He gathered them in steaming jungles, on high mountain meadows, on plains and river valleys. All over the globe he found trees, bushes, vines, and flowering plants that were useful to him. Most of the time he was searching for food, but in the course of tasting leaves, roots, and stems, he also learned that certain plants made him sick, and that others could cure him and take away pain. Some plants made him sweat, or reduced his fever, or took away headaches, or helped his colds. Other plants relieved stomach distress or quieted his nerves.

But superstition and magic were mixed up with man's first efforts to cure himself. To early man, mysterious powers seemed to rule the earth. These spirits sent him sunshine and rain, wind and storms, thunder and lightning. He was powerless before these natural things he did not understand. When he got sick, he blamed evil spirits; and the only known cure was to drive the evil spirits out of his body. To accomplish this, special medicine men dressed up in fearful-looking costumes and masks, painted their faces, and howled and cried

and banged on drums. But many of them also gave the sick man brews made of bitter herbs, which would be sure to disagree with the evil spirit and drive him out.

In this way, along with the chants and the magic and the ritual for treating disease, a knowledge of plant remedies grew. At first, only the plants with a strong odor or bitter taste attracted man's attention. Perhaps he learned many things from watching animals. What the dog or the deer ate when it was sick, might be good for him, too! By trial and error, primitive people came to use a great number of plants to heal their sick. If the juice of a plant, or a chewed leaf, or a piece of bark or root made the patient improve, it was used again. Of course, the sick man might have got better without having tasted a plant. But primitive people had no way of knowing this. They could not possibly have had our modern concept of the scientific method. Today we test the true value of a drug by experiment. We give a drug to one group of patients and, while keeping all other treatment identical, compare them with another group that does not receive the drug. We call the untreated group the *control* in our experiment. Without it, we cannot draw scientific conclusions.

Primitive people, therefore, accumulated a large number of plant drugs, many of which had no value at all. But in the course of time experience proved the value of certain plants. The knowledge of these was handed down by word of mouth from generation to generation.

We can get a glimpse into the primitive ways of using plants by studying people who are still living in primitive societies today. To cure themselves of disease, they use plants almost entirely. The roots, stems, barks, leaves, flowers, and seeds are still being chewed, dried, ground up, or brewed according to ancient recipes. In many places, the use of the plants is still combined with the same kind of ritual and magic that existed in early times.

Almost every Indian tribe of North America has ceremonies accompanying the gathering of plants. Usually a small hole is dug next to the plant, and some tobacco is placed in it as an offering to the spirit of the plant. Then the herb gatherer lights his pipe and smokes, and prays to the spirits that govern vegetation. He leaves the first plant in the ground and then searches out another plant of the same kind and gathers it.

American Indians believe their knowledge of plants came to them from the spirits. An Algonquin Indian legend tells how disease was sent to man by the wild animals, who were angered by the cruelties man practiced on them. The chipmunk, however, told man about this, and the other animals gave him his stripes as punishment. But after the chipmunk recovered from his punishment, he called together the vegetable kingdom, and at this gathering the plant spirits offered to man their healing juices to cure him of the diseases sent by animals.

Other Indian legends tell how great spirits descended to earth and showed wise Mother Earth the medicine bag, with its roots, leaves, and fruits. Mother Earth takes charge of

13

them. Then the spirits appear before the original forefathers of the tribe and instruct them in the uses of plants for medicine and in the proper ceremonies that must accompany the use of each.

From other Indian stories we discover that they must have learned much from their observation of animals. Chippewa legends tell how the best remedies were received from the bear. "The bear," they say, "pays attention to herbs. It eats roots from the earth, and acorns, berries, and cherries. It is an animal well acquainted with herbs." In spite of the legendary origins of these herbs, and the magic involved in their use, Indians built up an imposing list of plant remedies for their ills. There were eighty-eight plants to use against colds, one hundred and thirteen plants to reduce fever, one hundred and one plants with which to treat wounds, forty-one plants to calm the nerves, sixty-eight plants to act as laxatives, and over a hundred from which to pick remedies for stomach-ache. Each tribe had its own long lists of plants for the treatment of various ailments. These varied greatly, of course, with the area in which the tribes lived. One plant common to many North American Indian tribes was willow bark for rheumatism and joint pains. Perhaps the Indians originally chose this plant because they thought the willow's flexibility would be transferred to the stiff joints of a person sick with rheumatism. But

today we know why this remedy worked. Willow bark contains a pain-killing chemical—salicin—related to the substance present in today's aspirin.

South American Indians have also taught us a great deal about plant remedies. One tribe, the Collahuaya Indians, are called the wandering druggists of the Amazon, because they peddle the herbs they find in the tropical rain forest up and down the Amazon River. Dr. Henry Rusby of the Columbia University College of Pharmacy went to the Bolivian jungle about fifty years ago to study the plants used by this tribe and, among other things, found them using a tree bark to relieve "chest tightness." Dr. Rusby studied this bark (cocillana), and introduced it in a medicine for coughs. But this is only one of the many drugs the Collahuayans have given us.

Primitive tribes in Africa know every useful plant, bush, and tree in their jungles, fields, and plains, and use many of them as medicines to cure their fevers, colds, snake bites, and digestive disorders.

On isolated islands sprinkled all over the surface of the globe, people depend on native plants to cure themselves. This is true, too, of isolated parts of many countries. In these places, old folk remedies are still used.

Scientists today are paying new attention to these old remedies, for modern chemistry is throwing new light on them. In

16

China and India new tests have been made of ancient herb cures. The drug plants of Africa are being reviewed. In the Ukraine region of the Soviet Union, new studies have been made of the folk medicine practiced by peasants in the villages. In the United States today we are studying the drug lore of the Indian tribes. Many of the plants may turn out to be of little value. But some may yield the wonder drugs of tomorrow.

CHAPTER 2

From Stems and Roots to Pills and Powders

THE plant remedies of primitive societies, handed down by word of mouth from generation to generation, gradually became part of the knowledge of ancient civilizations. They were described in ancient books, on Egyptian papyri, on Babylonian clay tablets, and on temple walls.

Plant drugs were written about in China 5000 years ago. The first god of healing was Emperor Shen Nung, who, according to legend, tried out the medicinal value of hundreds of herbs. He is supposed to have described 250 plants in the first Chinese herbal, written about 2700 B.C. This work became the foundation of all later Chinese works on plants. The most famous of these later works is the Great Herbal, the Pen-Ts'ao of Kang-Mu published in 1596 during the Ming dynasty. All the plant lore of China was collected in this fifty-two-volume work. Over a thousand plants were listed, with

their history, the prescribed dosage, and the methods of preparation. Some of these same herbal remedies are being used in China today, along with the most modern twentieth-century medicine.

In India, too, plant medicine was an ancient art. The *Vedas,* the earliest sacred writings of Hinduism, have many references to plants. One beautiful poem is entitled "To a magical plant, that it heal a broken bone." It appeals to a plant to make the bone whole again.

> "Join thou together hair with hair,
> Join thou together skin with skin.
> Let blood and bone grow strong in thee.
> Unite the broken part, O plant!"

In another poem, "A Charm to Grow Hair," we find the lines:

> "Thy hair where it is falling off, and
> with the roots is torn away,
> I wet and sprinkle with the plant, the
> remedy for all disease."

In later Hindu writings, plant remedies are described in

more detail together with the same mixture of charms and religious prayers that marked early medicine in all countries. The use of such remedies became the foundation of medical treatment in India and later intermingled with that of Egypt, Greece, and Rome.

In Egypt ancient inscriptions and pictures on temple and tomb walls tell of the use of herbs as far back as 3000 B.C. But the oldest manuscript on the subject is the Ebers Papyrus, written about 1500 B.C. It was named for Georg Ebers, the

German archaeologist, who bought it from an Arab who discovered it between the knees of a mummy in a tomb in Thebes. On this long yellowish-brown fine papyrus (paper made from the stem of the papyrus plant), there is a collection of over 800 prescriptions for different diseases. It tells how to treat the sting of a wasp and the bite of a crocodile. It describes medicines for headaches, heart trouble, sore throats, and other ills. Plants were the important ingredients in these prescriptions.

In ancient Babylonia information about medicinal plants was recorded on clay tablets and stone cylinders. The Code of Hammurabi, engraved about 2000 B.C., tells of the medicinal uses for many plants.

The Greeks learned much from the ancient writings in Egypt and Babylonia. Hippocrates, called the Father of Medicine, described the use of many plant drugs in the fifth century B.C. Aristotle's pupil, Theophrastus, wrote, about 300 B.C., an *Enquiry Into Plants.* This book sums up the knowledge of plants gained up to that time. The section on medicine lists 500 plants. In this work, Theophrastus talks of the root gatherers—special groups of men who gathered and prepared the roots of medicinal plants. These Greek root gatherers tried to surround their trade with mystery, in order to keep others from engaging in it. They invented stories about the dangers of herb gathering. "Peony fruits," they said, "must be collected at night. If

they are gathered in the daylight, the woodpecker might see and peck out the collector's eyes." They warned people not to gather a certain plant, because an eagle might pass which would result in the collector's death within the year! By means of such stories they kept other people from joining their select group.

Nothing much was added to Greek knowledge of medicinal plants during Roman times. But in about the year 77 A.D., Dioscorides described some five hundred plants and their uses, in a work that became very influential. For centuries afterward it was copied and translated into many languages. During the second century A.D. the last great ancient physician, Galen, wrote about five hundred works on medicine and physiology, and described the preparation of many plant medicines.

The term *Galenical* has been used up to modern times to describe medicines prepared according to the formula of Galen. Today the term is used to describe preparations that have organic ingredients (those derived from living organisms), rather than pure chemical ones.

Toward the end of the fifth century, Rome fell to the German Goths. During the centuries that followed, from about 500 A.D. to 1200 A.D., the knowledge of plant medicine did not advance much. Any progress that was made was due to the Arabs, who preserved and combined the plant knowledge gained from Greece, Egypt, India, China, and the Middle East. They spread this knowledge over the vast Empire, extending from Spain to the borders of China, which they conquered. They are credited with establishing the first drugstores in the world. In such shops in Baghdad, earthenware pots and jars and straw baskets carried the leaves, roots, flowers, seeds, and fruits of some of the 1400 different plants they used as medicine.

During this period, the knowledge of medicinal plants in Europe was kept alive in monasteries. In monastic herb gar-

dens medicinal plants were grown and used to prepare remedies for the sick. Inside the walls of the monasteries, ancient manuscripts on plants were translated into Latin and copied over and over. This slow, difficult way of writing books by hand came to an end in the middle of the fifteenth century, when printing with movable type was invented. From then on, in every country of Europe, herbals were printed. Like the ancient ones, they were books that described plants and their medicinal properties. But unlike the earlier ones, they were beautifully illustrated with pictures based on firsthand obser-

Woodcut from 15th century herbal

Qy commence la declaracıo des pzoprie tes du romanin. la fleur du romarı liee

vation of plants in nature, instead of being copies of other copies of plants from ancient manuscripts. If you look at one of these herbals of the fifteenth and sixteenth centuries, you will be amazed at the number of plants used for treating disease. You will find mixtures of fact and falsehood—because at that time it was not considered necessary or desirable to test a statement by experiment. Herb gathering and the use of herbs were still wrapped in superstition.

One of these superstitions in the sixteenth century was called the Doctrine of Signatures. According to this, every plant showed some sign of its intended use. If a plant had leaves shaped like the lobes of the liver, it was undoubtedly meant for diseases of the liver. If it had heart-shaped leaves, it was surely beneficial to the heart. Yellow plants must be for the cure of yellow diseases like jaundice. The aspen that quivered in the breezeless air was a plant for "shaking" diseases, like ague and palsy. Saxifrage, which grew among broken rocks and crumbled them, would crumble the stones in a man's kidney. We still have leftovers of the Doctrine of Signatures in the common names of many plants like heartsease, liver leaf, etc.

Typical of the superstitions of the time was the way in which the mandrake plant was regarded. This plant had a long, thick forked root that sometimes resembled the shape of the human body. It was considered a magical plant with great healing powers and had a reputation for producing sleep. Actually we know today that the root contains a powerful narcotic that acts on the nerves to relieve pain and induce sleep. But in those times such properties were regarded with fear and wonder. It was said that the mandrake plant gave off horrible shrieks when it was torn from the ground, and that to avoid turning mad, the plant gatherer had to stuff his ears with wax or wool. According to some stories, the plant gatherer would die within a year if he pulled up a mandrake plant.

Mandrake

Because of this, he generally tied the upper part of the plant to a dog and then encouraged the dog to run toward him and so uproot the plant.

Superstitious notions also clung to ways of collecting other plants. Some of these fanciful ideas can be traced back to the old Greek root-gatherer stories. But during the seventeenth century, herb gathering was chiefly associated with astrology. The moon, stars, and planets were said to govern the collection and use of plants. Typical directions were to "gather the plant at the rising of the Dog Star Sirius, when neither sun nor moon shines, with the left hand only." Nicholas Culpepper, in a famous seventeenth-century herbal still in print today, gives complicated directions for picking and using plants when the right planets are in the sky.

A prescription sent into a city pharmacy in the very early seventeenth century gives us some idea of the complicated mixtures popular at the time. "As a liniment for rheumatism," it says, "take three little newborn dogs and three living moles, one pound of earthworms, leaves of laurel, rosemary, mint, sweet marjoram, lavender, thyme, St.-John's-wort, of each a handful; boil these ingredients in three pounds of oil mixed with common wine until the latter is consumed; then pour out and express liquid from solids; add to the liquid yellow wax and goose fat, each 10 ounces. Apply to the skin heated before a fire; repeat as often as required."

Mixed in with the superstition and magical nonsense, there was a core of truth in the herb medicine that was practiced. Europeans of the time had some excellent remedies hidden among an enormous number of ineffective ones. As Rudyard Kipling said, "Anything green that grew out of the mould, was an excellent drug to our fathers of old."

A whole new collection of plants was added to the known remedies of the Old World with the discovery of America. Spanish explorers found the Indians of Central and South

America using strange new plants, and they mentioned them in their early reports. Dr. Nicolás Monardes of Seville, Spain, collected such reports and gathered additional information. He spoke to ship captains, travelers, and missionaries who had been to the New World. He studied shipments of medical plants sent from there. He then published the first accounts of native plant remedies from South America, Mexico, and the West Indies. In *Joyfull Newes out of the New Found World,* published in 1545, he tells of the virtues of the strange new herbs and their use in medicine.

The first book about medicinal plants actually written in America was the Aztec Herbal of 1552. The author was an Aztec Indian doctor, Martín de la Cruz, who was studying at the college of Santa Cruz in Mexico. The book was translated into Latin by a fellow Aztec, Juannes Badianus. The curative value of hundreds of native Mexican plants was pictured and described in this beautiful manuscript. The people of Europe were astonished at the number and variety of plants the Aztec Indians used to cure their sick. Many of the New World plants were added to the European list of drugs.

When settlers came to North America, they brought with them a knowledge of herbs from the Old World, but they found the North American Indians using entirely different plants. The Indians did not easily part with their secrets. Some

Tolohaxihuitl.   Nexehuac.

Contra laterum dolorem.

Lateralem dolorem herba nomine Tolohaxihuitl
& Nexehuac magna frita admotaqi anferunt.

A page from the Badianus manuscript

few of them did teach their art to the pioneers, and gradually people became acquainted with the properties of many of the native American plants. At that early period in the life of this country, anyone who knew one curative plant from another and how to use it was a welcome settler and could function as

a doctor. But most pioneer families treated themselves. They kept a stock of herbs on hand, and turned to home medical books to find out how to brew them and how much to use.

A typical book was the *Indian Vegetable Family Instructer*, published in 1836. In its introduction, the author says: "Our fields abound with vegetable medicine, and the fertile meadows produce many a valuable root. Root and herbs are at the command of every one and nature's prescriptions are all free gratis." In its contents you can find vegetable remedies for coughs, for deafness, and for ringing in the ears. You can also find pills for hysteria, etc.

Many households worked out their own mixtures and sold them to their neighbors. A particular mixture of boneset, sage, and bloodroot, for instance, might be called better than any other. But so might any combination of herbs. Hundreds of untrained people mixed up their own plant formulas and claimed that they would cure any and every disease. Many took their cures with them on wagons and traveled through American towns, stopping here and there to put on medicine shows. They made great use of the respect people had for Indian cures. They called their medicines Indian Tonic or Indian Remedy or Indian Elixir. The use of the word *Indian* seemed to work like magic.

In the nineteenth century a breath of fresh air from the world of science began to blow away the prevailing foggy ideas about herb remedies and their uses. This happened when chemists began to isolate the active chemicals contained in various plants. The first work of this kind was done by a young pharmacist named Frederick Sertuerner, who isolated morphine from the crude drug, opium. This was followed by the work of Pierre Pelletier and Joseph Caventou, two French chemists who extracted many other alkaloids from plants. These alkaloids were organic chemicals found in plants that were alkaline (the opposite of acid) in nature. They discovered the pure alkaloid, quinine, in cinchona bark; the pure alkaloid, strychnine, in the Strychnos plant; the pure emetine in ipecac plants. Other research workers then found atropine in belladonna, ephedrine in the ephedra plant, etc. By the middle of the nineteenth century, many alkaloids were known. Other kinds of compounds were found too, and soon many hundreds of pure chemicals were isolated from plants and put into pills or liquid medicines.

Where the natural drug is used, the guesswork in the preparation of the plant material is eliminated by the setting up of certain definite government standards. These are described in books called pharmacopoeias. The plants are described accurately, together with the parts of the plants used, the standards to test their purity, the methods of preparation, and the average doses.

But the tendency now is for the natural drugs to be replaced by the active chemicals in them. Hundreds of tons of plants are

converted every year into pure chemicals. For example, it takes about a hundred pounds of cinchona bark to make five pounds of pure quinine.

Once the active chemical in a plant is found, chemists analyze its structure. They break down a complex compound into simple compounds. Then they try to put these pieces back together in the right order. Sometimes they manage to synthesize a compound from simple things like water, salts, carbon dioxide, and oxygen. In this way the chemist tries to duplicate the elaborate processes that go on in plants.

CHAPTER 3

Plants That Made Medical History

PIECES of bark from a tree, and underground roots that store up precious chemicals have made medical history.

The Quinine Story

Malaria is a disease which, since early times, had plagued all tropical countries. The word *malaria* actually means "bad air" and describes what most people thought to be the cause of the disease: poisonous vapors that rose from the swamps. We know now that a parasitic protozoan carried by the anopheles mosquito causes malaria. We did not find this out until about 1900. For hundreds of years before that, people in warm, low countries searched for plants that might help cure the fevers and chills that went with this disease.

A specific cure for it lay in the bark of tall trees that grew in South America. In secluded parts of the forest slopes on the eastern side of the Andes, these beautiful trees grew among hundreds of other kinds of trees in the forest. How did men discover that this particular tree, with its straight trunk, dark waxy green leaves, and clusters of bright rose flowers, could cure malaria? Actually, we do not know, but probably the Indians who lived in these forests were the first to become familiar with its curative powers.

These trees, now called Cinchona, got their name from a romantic story about the Countess of Chinchón, the wife of the Spanish Viceroy in Lima, Peru. She was supposed to have been stricken with malaria in the year 1630, and to have been cured with potions made from the bark of these trees. The Countess is said to have been so grateful that she carried the bark to Spain to relieve the sufferings of malaria patients there.

Historians have carefully checked this story and found it to be untrue, but it was widely accepted at the time. Linnaeus, the scientist who classified and gave Latin names to the members of the plant kingdom, believed this story and named the tree Cinchona in honor of the Countess of Chinchón. By mistake, he left out the first *h* and all other scientists copied the name as he gave it.

Accurate historical records do tell us that the Jesuit priests in Lima, Peru, knew about the cinchona bark in the middle of

the seventeenth century. For a long time it was called Jesuits' bark, because Jesuit Fathers helped to spread the knowledge of its curative powers to Spain, France, and Italy.

By the nineteenth century the use of cinchona bark had spread all over the world. Men in chemical laboratories searched for the active chemicals in the bark, and in 1820 Pelletier and Caventou extracted a sticky gum from the bark and named it quinine. Medical tests made with the new substance showed that this was the effective agent in the bark, which cured malaria.

The trees that grew in South America were the only source of this great new chemical. England and France wanted to break the South American monopoly and start plantations of their own in their colonies in India and Java. Both countries sent plant hunters out on expeditions to the Andes to get seeds and plants of the Cinchona tree.

In 1829 a Dutch botanist, J. K. Hasskarl, managed to get seed plants out of South America, but the plants did not survive the voyage across the Pacific to Java. The seeds were planted, but it took years to find out that they had come from a species that was not rich in quinine. Another Dutch botanist went to South America in 1849, but his seeds, too, were not the valuable kind. Meanwhile, the English sent several expeditions. The scientists on these expeditions had to work under difficulties in the dense, steaming jungles, collecting seeds and cuttings secretly. For by this time South American countries were alert to the danger of having their monopoly broken by the export of seeds and plants of their precious trees. The English finally smuggled seeds and cuttings to India, but some were planted in unsuitable locations and others turned out to be quinine-poor species.

Meanwhile, an Englishman, Charles Ledger, who lived in Peru and did business there, had become familiar with Cinchona trees whose bark yielded great quantities of quinine. He gathered the seeds of these trees and sent them to his brother in London. His brother offered to sell them to the British government, which, however, declined to buy them, expecting at that time to get plenty of seeds and cuttings from its own expeditions. Ledger's brother then went to Holland to offer his brother's seeds to the Dutch. They bought one pound of these seeds in 1865 and sent them to Java, where they were planted. They germinated, grew well, and turned out to be the best quinine-yielding species in the world. The Dutch government laid the basis for its monopoly of the world's quinine with this one pound of seed!

German chemists studied the chemical structure of quinine, trying to create a synthetic chemical. They finally succeeded in producing atabrine, which acted like quinine in the treatment of malaria. The second World War cut off German supplies and forced American scientists to prepare atabrine themselves. It was used throughout the malaria-infested battle zones of North Africa, Guadalcanal, Burma, and the Philippines.

Chemical laboratories continued to search for other synthetic substitutes for quinine and in the 1940's came up with three new synthetics: chloroquine, exychloroquine, and pentaquine. Then the British discovered paludrine. Now most of these synthetic remedies for malaria have yielded their place to daraprim, the newest synthetic to come from the laboratory to displace the natural chemical found in the bark of Cinchona trees.

The Cortisone Story

In 1949 an exciting new medical discovery was announced in the newspapers. Dr. Philip S. Hench of the Mayo Clinic in Rochester, Minnesota, reported successful results in the treatment of rheumatoid arthritis with a new chemical substance. People crippled with this disease could walk again! The chemical was the hormone cortisone, secreted by the adrenal glands of cattle, and had been discovered by another Mayo Clinic scientist, Dr. Edward Kendall, in 1935. Its use for treating arthritis created great excitement. Doctors all over the country wanted to try the new wonder drug. But the new hormone was scarce. It could be manufactured from a natural compound found in the bile of oxen. But it took the bile of 4000 cattle to make only one gram of cortisone! Besides, it took thirty-two complicated chemical steps to produce it. The demand for the drug was great, however, and set off a race to find other materials from which cortisone could be manufactured. At this point scientists turned to the plant kingdom to search for possible chemicals that could be converted into cortisone.

Suddenly, a tropical plant, Strophanthus, became famous as a possible source of cortisone. It was said to have a chemical in it that could simplify the manufacture of the new drug. African tribes had been using the plant for centuries as an arrow poison. In 1861 the famous explorer, Dr. David Livingstone, had discovered this and reported it to the world. Medical trials with the seeds of Strophanthus showed that it contained a powerful medicine for the heart. But its possible value as a starting material for cortisone put Strophanthus in a new light, and set off a search for species rich in the desired chemical.

Several expeditions were organized to explore the remote jungles of Africa for Strophanthus. Collections were made of the seeds of these woody climbers that scrambled up to the tops of trees in equatorial forests. The different species were carefully studied and analyzed, and although one species was found to be very rich in the chemical that could be changed into cortisone, this species was very rare and could not be cultivated.

Meanwhile, other studies pushed the Strophanthus plant into the background. Russell E. Marker of Pennsylvania State College had been studying substances called steroids. These were compounds found in plants that were chemically very similar to animal hormones. Marker was able to take a plant steroid and convert it into an animal hormone. This itself was a great achievement and provided a brand-new source of animal hormones for the drug industry. The plant source he found richest in the needed steroid was the root of a yam, Dioscorea. Marker and other researchers who were looking for a plant source for the hormone cortisone were quick to realize that this Mexican yam was a plant to investigate. Several research teams began to look for a short route to cortisone from this plant. Finally they did produce it from this dark-brown yam from the jungles of Mexico. Mass production of cortisone was started, and gradually arthritis sufferers received this drug, which relieved their pain and restored the use of their limbs.

Once again, a plant came to hold a high place among the

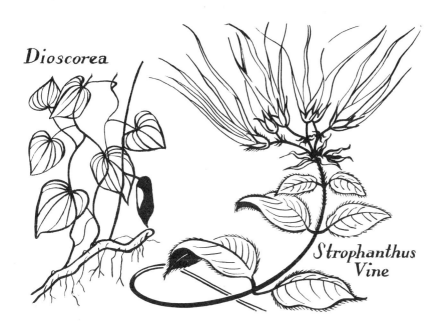

Dioscorea

Strophanthus Vine

important drug plants of the world. Now other plant sources have been found. Besides yams, agaves, yuccas, and sisal plants are used to supply an inexhaustible amount of the low-cost raw material needed to manufacture cortisone.

The Rauwolfia Story

Rauwolfia, the snakeroot plant, made headlines too. This plant has been growing on the slopes of the mountains in India for thousands of years. Its long tapering snakelike root has been valued there since ancient times as a cure for poisonous snake bites and fevers. Many legends were told about the strange and magical powers of this plant. One said that the mongoose ate this plant to gain the strength to overcome the cobra in battle. Another legend told of curing madness with its roots. One of its names in the ancient Hindu books of medicine is Chandra, meaning moon. This name is said to indicate its use in the "moon's disease," or lunacy. At one time or another it was mentioned as a cure for practically every disease. It was prescribed for epilepsy, dysentery, cholera, hemorrhages, headaches, and many other ailments. Most of these stories arose because the root did have great sedative powers.

The plant was given the scientific name Rauwolfia after Leonhard Rauwolf, a German physician and botanist who made an expedition to Asia and Africa in the latter part of the sixteenth century and found and described the plant. Two hundred years ago in Europe it was claimed that the drug relieved anxiety. But in spite of its long use in India and its introduction into Europe, nothing much was heard of this plant until the 1930's, when Indian research workers started a systematic study of their ancient medical plants.

In 1931 two Indian scientists isolated the crystals of two chemicals from Rauwolfia roots and described their action in lowering high blood pressure. They also noted that the pow-

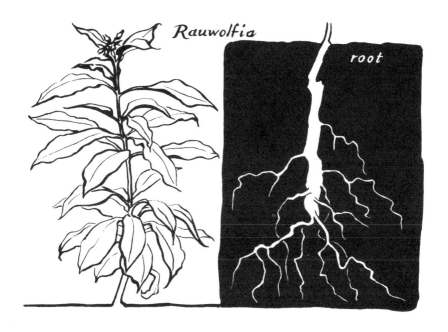

Rauwolfia

root

dered root of Rauwolfia could calm a violent maniac. They called Rauwolfia "a drug of rare merit" and urged other research workers to test it. No other country took up the challenge, but the Indian scientists continued their work. They tried the powdered root on thousands of high-blood-pressure patients. It brought down the blood pressure of even the most serious cases! Dr. Vakil of Bombay finally published his findings on high blood pressure in 1949 in a British medical journal of great influence. Rauwolfia was on its way to fame.

Dr. Vakil's reports received the attention of British and

American doctors. Several doctors in Boston tried tablets of powdered Rauwolfia on their high-blood-pressure patients and found it remarkably effective. When their work was published in American medical magazines and Rauwolfia was tried by other doctors, it started a mass demand for the drug.

The powdered root was still being used, because none of the chemicals that had been extracted from the root seemed to have the power possessed by the whole drug. Some important ingredient of the root had not yet been discovered. In 1944 Indian scientists came to realize that there was an active principle of the drug hidden in the brown, muddy resin of the root. They were unable to analyze it further. It was not until 1952 that two Swiss chemists, using new chemical techniques for analysis, found some new white crystals in the resin that carried the principal effect of the whole Rauwolfia root. They named their discovery reserpine.

Now chemists studied the new chemical and worked out ways to produce it in large quantities. Batches of it were tried out in hospitals all over the world and found to be an effective treatment for high blood pressure.

In all the studies of high blood pressure, doctors noted the calming effect of the powdered root or the pure chemical reserpine. Now doctors in state mental hospitals tried it out. The results were dramatic. Disturbances were cut down. Noisy wards grew quiet. Reserpine was the first tranquilizing drug to help mentally ill patients back to normal life. It began a whole new approach to the treatment of mental disease.

New compounds that soothe troubled minds have been synthesized in the laboratory. These new compounds, along with reserpine, have helped millions of people suffering from high blood pressure and nervous tension. The new compounds are also leading to exciting new discoveries of the chemistry of the brain. These in turn will open the door to a vast field in the chemical treatment of mental disorders.

The Chaulmoogra Story

The story of the chaulmoogra tree is another instance of the introduction into modern medicine of a plant used since ancient times. Stories of a mysterious tree whose seeds were a remedy for leprosy were recorded in ancient Hindu books. An old legend from Burma tells of Piya, the daughter of a king, who contracted leprosy. Her brothers and sisters took her into a jungle and left her in a cave. At the same time, Rama, once the king of a neighboring state, was living in the jungle because he, too, had leprosy and had exiled himself. He fed himself on herbs and roots and on the fruits and leaves of the

Chaulmoogra Seeds

chaulmoogra tree. After a while he found himself completely cured. Piya was living in a cave near Rama's tree home, but neither knew that the other was there. One day a tiger came prowling near Piya's cave. Piya screamed, and Rama came to the rescue. He fed her on the fruits and leaves of the tree that had cured him, and she, too, became healthy again. And, the story goes, Rama founded a new city in the jungle area he had inhabited while a leper.

This legend gives us some idea of the ancient use of this plant. The western world did not hear of it until about 1856, when English doctors traveling in the Far East learned of its use in the treatment of leprosy.

The seeds of the chaulmoogra tree could be bought in the market places of cities in Burma, but the actual tree that bore the seeds had not been found by plant scientists. In 1920 the United States government sent out an expedition headed by Joseph F. Rock to search for these trees.

He first found relatives of the chaulmoogra tree growing in Siam. Their seeds also produced oil capable of curing leprosy, but Rock continued his search. Later on, after many adventures in the forests of Burma, he came across the true chaulmoogra tree. He sent seeds to Hawaii, where they were cultivated.

For some time Hawaiian hospitals had been carrying on special studies on the treatment of lepers. They used the crude chaulmoogra oil pressed from the seeds and gave it by mouth. Although the treatment was effective, it often made the patient extremely nauseated. Finally a refined thin oil was obtained from chaulmoogra seeds and this could be injected directly into the blood stream. At the Kalihi Hospital in Honolulu the new treatment was tried out. In one fourteen-month period ending March 15, 1921, fifty per cent of the leprosy patients recovered! The leper no longer had to be an outcast.

Today new chemicals having the same effect as chaulmoogra oil have been synthesized in the laboratory.

CHAPTER 4

Plant Medicines in Use

THERE is scarcely a plant that has not been tried out somewhere in the world to relieve sickness. Some were considered cure-alls. Some were specific cures for colds, or heart disease, or fevers, or stomach distress. Only a few of these are still in much use today.

Tonics

Every country in the world has some plants they use as general tonics and cure-alls. In China ginseng has been used for thousands of years. According to legend, the wail of a man was heard night after night at the back of a certain person's house in Shansi. People searched for the sound but could find nothing. Finally someone found a remarkable ginseng plant with a root in the shape of a man with arms and legs. After this the wail was never heard again, and the root was called the "spirit of the ground." It is amazing how similar these stories of ginseng are to the ones about the mandrake plant in Europe. The mandrake, too, had a root that sometimes resembled a human body. It, too, shrieked. It, too, was regarded as a sacred plant—although perhaps for a better reason, for the mandrake had the power to produce sleep. Although scientists have analyzed the chemicals in the ginseng plant, they have so far found nothing that might have given this plant its fine reputation. But old Chinese books claimed it was a "tonic to the five viscera, brightening the eye, invigorating the body, and prolonging life." Even today in China there are plenty of people who ask for ginseng when they are ill.

Sassafras was a favorite spring tonic throughout North America. This old Iroquois cure-all created a stir in Europe in colonial days. Fantastic stories about how this tree cured almost every sickness reached Europe and gave it a place among the first exports from the Jamestown colony in Virginia. Country people today are still boiling the yellow blossoms, the oddly shaped leaves, and the inner bark of the root, and passing the tea around at the beginning of spring to help get rid of the winter doldrums. There doesn't seem to be any real value to this plant except as a good-smelling tea that makes you perspire.

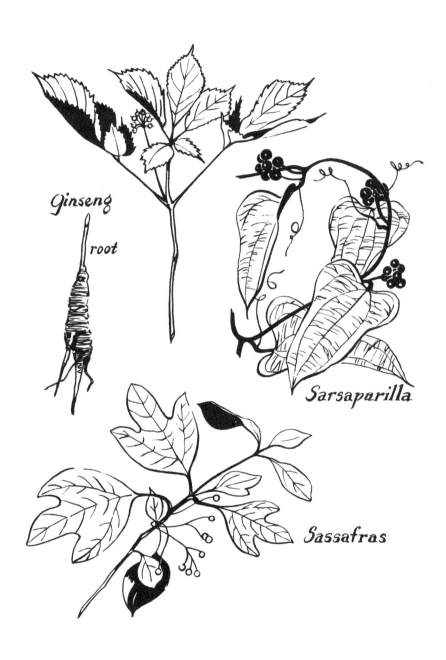

Ginseng

root

Sarsaparilla

Sassafras

Sarsaparilla had its day as a tonic too. The root of the climbing plant Smilax, found in South America, was also called a cure for almost every disease. We still don't know all there is to know about this plant. It is used in medicine today in combination with other drugs to treat a number of blood diseases.

Calamus root, or sweet flag, was an outstanding general remedy used by many North American Indian tribes. It seems to have some soothing properties, which are being investigated today.

In the Ukraine the white water lily ranks first as a cure for many diseases. The chemical substances isolated from this plant have been shown to affect the heart and the nervous system.

Isolated areas in every country in South America, Africa, India, Europe, and Asia have their own favorite tonic plants.

Laxatives

Aloes from Africa and Arabia, senna from India and Egypt, psyllium from Europe and Asia, ipecac from South America, cascara from the west coast of North America, rhubarb from China, and castor oil from India are still used today for stomach-aches and other digestive disorders.

When the thick lance-shaped spiny leaves of aloes are cut, a juice with laxative properties oozes out. Recently the fresh leaf and the leaf pulp of aloes have been found to heal X-ray burns.

Senna, from the dried leaves of the Cassia plant, was used as far back as the ninth century by Arabian physicians. They introduced it to Europe, where it became the favorite strong laxative during the Middle Ages.

We are all familiar with castor oil today. The small tree whose seeds contain the oil has been known since ancient times. It has deeply lobed leaves and clusters of spiny fruits which, upon ripening, split and shoot out the big mottled seeds from which the oil is pressed.

Dried ripe psyllium seeds are favored by many as a mild laxative. These seeds are surrounded by a sticky mucilage, which swells in water to a thick layer of jelly. In the intestines, their smooth bulk helps to move things along.

Chinese rhubarb was famous as a laxative 5000 years ago. It was carried on caravan routes across Persia to Mediterranean ports. Its reddish-brown roots were prized throughout the Middle Ages, and still are today, for use as a bitter tonic and laxative.

Cascara is a native American laxative. Mexicans and California priests learned about it from the Indians in the early

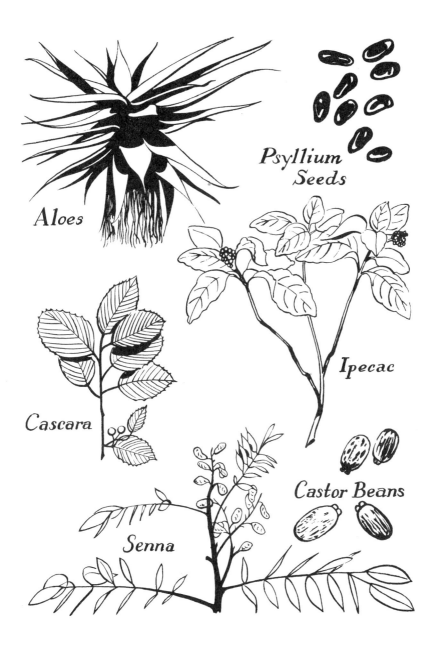

Aloes

Psyllium
Seeds

Cascara

Ipecac

Senna

Castor Beans

part of the ninetenth century. Seventy-five years later, the plant was introduced into medical practice. The drug comes from the bark of a tree that grows in river valleys on the west coast. The bark is peeled in the spring, when the tree is growing vigorously, and is then dried and stored.

Brazilian Indians were treating dysentery with ipecac, from the twisted roots of a creeping plant, for centuries before this drug was recognized by doctors. Dysentery is a disease that attacks and inflames the lining of the digestive tract. Ipecac became famous in the seventeenth century as a cure for this disease. At that time a young Dutch physician, Helvetius, tried out some of the roots of this plant which had been imported from South America. His experiments worked, and he plastered the street corners of Paris with announcements of the successful use of this new drug. News of it reached the French court, where dysentery was creating havoc. His new plant healed many people, and Helvetius gained fame for his wonderful cure. Today we know that emetine, a chemical obtained from the bark of this plant, is the active agent. It is much used today in the treatment of amoebic dysentery.

Heart Medicines

The foxglove plant, or digitalis, was famous in folklore and old wives' tales, and later became one of the great heart medicines of the world.

Foxglove

This tall, stately plant grew wild over the greater part of Europe, but it was cultivated in gardens for its spikes of beautiful bell-like flowers. For centuries every English household knew that this plant was a cure for the disease called dropsy. A person with dropsy had a puffed-up body filled with watery liquids. Nobody knew then that this was due to weak heart muscles that couldn't push the blood along fast enough to keep the fluids moving through the tissues. But they did know that the leaves of the foxglove could magically drain the body of this extra fluid and restore a person to health. A Shropshire woman brought her old family prescription for dropsy to a young village doctor, William Withering. He examined the list of plants in the prescription and decided that foxglove was probably the important ingredient. He tried it out on his patients, experimented with doses, and in 1785 laid down the general principles of its use.

The active chemical in the plant was discovered in France and Germany and called digitalin. It cures dropsy because it makes the heart beat strongly and pump the blood along so that the extra fluids in the tissues are removed. Because digitalin strengthens the contracting force of the heart muscles and makes the heart work more efficiently, it has become one of the most valuable of present-day heart medicines.

Other plants were also used for the heart. There were squill (the Mediterranean sea onion), the flowering oleander, the lily of the valley, and the Strophanthus vine, which all contain chemicals that strengthen the action of the heart.

Medicines for Coughs, Colds, and Asthma

Asthma and hay fever are ancient troubles, and the plant remedies for them are ancient too. For 5000 years in China they have been using a plant known as *ma huang*. This plant, Ephedra, became known to Western scientists fairly recently. In 1887 a Japanese scientist showed that its slender green jointed stems contain ephedrine—a most effective chemical in the treatment of asthma, hay fever, and other congestions of the nose, throat, and chest. Today the natural drug is not used much, because ephedrine can be made synthetically in chemical laboratories.

The North American Indians used another plant, Lobelia. It was commonly called Indian tobacco, because the Indians smoked the dried leaves as a substitute for tobacco. Another American plant used for asthma was the thorn apple or Jimson weed. This plant, with its white funnel-like flowers and prickly thorny fruit, was known to Indian tribes of Arizona and Mexico before the discovery of America. Jamestown settlers in Virginia collected it as a pot herb and discovered it to be poisonous if taken in large quantities. It became known as the Jamestown weed, and the name was later shortened to Jimson weed. People smoked its leaves to relieve asthma congestion. Many important chemicals were found in this plant. One of

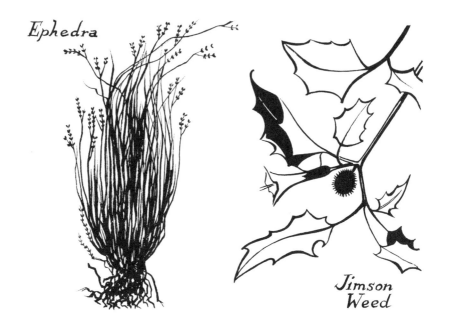

Ephedra

Jimson Weed

them, scopolamine, has been used to induce twilight sleep (partial anesthesia) in childbirth, and to treat bomb shock, seasickness, and airsickness. Another chemical obtained from this plant is atropine, which is used to enlarge the pupil in eye examinations.

The large dark-green leaves of the eucalyptus tree contain a pungent oil that is used as a spray for colds and sore throats. From the oil of turpentine tapped from pine trees, comes terpin hydrate, a common remedy for coughs and colds.

Fever Plants

People all over the world found plants that reduced fevers. Cinchona, which contains quinine, was the most famous of these. North American Indians used the blue cohosh plant and called it their "great fever medicine." They also used the leaves and berries of wintergreen to break a fever or cold. Oil of wintergreen is still used today as a liniment for aching muscles or in steaming teas. Africans, Brazilians, Malayans, and other peoples in every country have their own favorite fever-reducing plants. But today aspirin made synthetically in factories is the favorite fever medicine all over the world.

Painkillers

Long before any anesthetics were used in surgery, people knew about the roots or leaves or berries of certain plants that could kill pain. The most famous of these are opium and cocaine—from opposite sides of the world.

The very oldest records of plant drugs mention the opium poppy and its sleep-producing property. This spiny-leaved plant has large delicate pink flowers. Its stems, leaves, flowers, and seeds contain no very active chemicals. The seeds, in fact,

Opium Poppy

have a pleasant flavor and are sprinkled on rolls, bread, and cakes. But after the petals fall from the flowers, a powerful milky juice forms in the unripe fruits or capsules. The method of collecting it is simple. The capsules are slit with sharp knives, and the sticky milky juice oozes out and thickens on the pod. This is scraped off and changes into dark-colored opium.

The alkaloid morphine was extracted from opium. It proved to be a wonderful medical aid, giving sleep to people racked with pain. But as time went on, it was shown to be dangerous, too. At first it takes only a small quantity to produce pleasant dreams and deep sleep. But the drug is habit-forming. Gradually larger and larger doses must be taken in order to get the same sensations. By this time the desire for the drug is so great that all normal life becomes impossible. In the hands of a doctor, morphine is a most important plant drug; but its use has to be strictly controlled by law, because its continued use leads to serious disturbances that eventually make a wreck of the addict.

News of a strange new pain-relieving plant came to Europe shortly after the conquest of Peru. The Spanish conquerors found the Incas of Peru cultivating this coca plant on the eastern slopes of the Andes. It was an entirely different plant from the cacao plant from which cocoa was made. All kinds of stories about the coca plant were told in Europe. It was said that the leaf of this plant destroyed fatigue, hunger, and thirst; that men could labor for long hours without food and drink if they chewed the leaf with a bit of lime; that this divine plant of the Incas gave men almost magical endurance. In high mountain altitudes they felt no cold. In tropical valleys they could endure great heat. These stories about the coca plant created great excitement in Europe. But it took several hundred years to discover the real truth about these marvelous claims.

Coca Leaves

In 1860 the active chemical substance in the leaves was isolated and named cocaine. In 1884 three German doctors in Vienna started to investigate the effects of cocaine. They rediscovered what other investigators had been saying: "Cocaine can numb the skin, the mouth, the eyes; it can wipe out pain!" They tried a few drops in an animal's eye, and found they could perform any kind of eye operation without the animal's feeling any pain. Finally their tests on patients in an eye clinic proved that cocaine really was a good local anesthetic that made eye surgery possible for the first time. This report on cocaine led to other tests. Dentists found they could deaden pain with it. Doctors found they could introduce cocaine into the spinal cord and operate painlessly with the aid of this new spinal anesthetic.

While cocaine was being introduced into medicine as a local anesthetic, it was also being tried out on various diseases. People claimed it could cure anything from tuberculosis to diabetes. But gradually it became clear that here was another habit-forming drug. People who took cocaine for a long time became addicted to its use and were unable to stop it. Because of this, scientists looked for other local painkillers, and in 1904 Novocain was synthesized. It, too, could kill pain, but it did not have the dangerous habit-forming property of cocaine.

Today farm hands in Argentina and tin miners in Bolivia and Peru carry a daily ration of coca leaves to sustain them in their day's work. Opinion is divided as to whether coca-leaf chewing is bad. Some say that the small amount of cocaine in the natural coca leaf is not enough to produce any bad effect and that, in such amounts, it is not a habit-forming drug. Others maintain that cocaine, in any amount, is a dangerous habit-forming drug which should be avoided.

There are many other medicinal plants besides the ones mentioned in this chapter. Those to be discussed in the next chapter were first used as poisons.

CHAPTER 5

Plants That Can Be Poisonous

It was easy for men to find out that certain plants can be irritating when touched. The oil of a plant like poison ivy causes a powerful itching and blistering of the skin, and people have learned to avoid it and other similar plants. But most poisonous plants are harmful only when eaten. A long time ago men found out which plants made people sick and sometimes killed them.

Monkshood has been known to be poisonous since ancient times in India and China. Although every part of this plant contains a poison called aconite, it is still grown in gardens for the sake of its lovely flowers. People in India once used a paste of the mashed underground stems to smear on the tips of their spears and hunting arrows. Sometimes they used it to poison wells that might be used by enemies. When British invading armies came to India, they found wells poisoned with crushed aconite. This poison causes difficult breathing, a slow, weak pulse, and final collapse, if nothing is done to counteract it.

Another poisonous plant well known in India is the poison nut tree strychnos which resembles our dogwood. The fruit looks like a small orange. Inside its white flesh are the flat seeds from which the poison strychnine is extracted. It became known in the sixteenth century, and from that time on it has been used to poison rats and other undesirable animals. When rabbits overran Australia, strychnine was the principal poison used to exterminate them.

On Babylonian clay tablets there are records of several poisonous plants. One of these is henbane. *Bane* means a poison substance that destroys life, and so the word *henbane* tells you that this plant was known to be poisonous to hens. The Babylonians used it in small amounts 3000 years ago to relieve toothache. It was also known to produce sleep and hallucinations or visions. In *The Arabian Nights,* one story tells how henbane was mixed with firewood and burned, till the smoke entered the nostrils of the guards, who all fell asleep from the fumes of the drug. Another story from the Middle Ages tells how the monks in an ancient monastery were served with henbane instead of a harmless vegetable, and how they were seized with hallucinations. They heard bells ringing everywhere, and

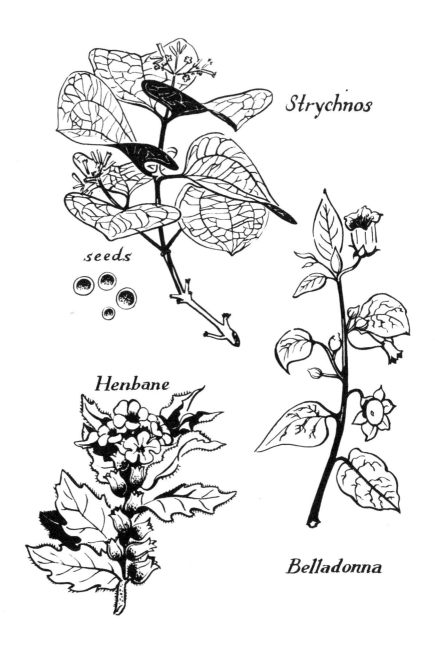

Strychnos

seeds

Henbane

Belladonna

Poison
Hemlock

turned the whole monastery into something like a lunatic asylum. Henbane even *looks* like a plant to stay away from. It has sticky, hairy leaves, sinister yellow flowers with purple veins, and a heavy bad odor.

The Greeks knew several plant poisons, but used poison hemlock the most. This plant is not the same as the tall hemlock tree of northern forests. It resembles Queen Anne's lace, with finely cut leaves and small white flowers. The poison is in the root, leaves, and fruit. The Greeks gave it to Socrates when they put him to death in 399 B.C. Old men of the Greek island of Ceos were said to drink a cup of poison hemlock when they were of no further use to the state. The poison causes a paralysis of the muscles. First the legs and arms are paralyzed and finally the chest muscles, making it impossible to breathe.

The Romans were acquainted with poison hemlock, henbane, aconite, and a plant known as belladonna, or deadly nightshade. Plutarch, who wrote about the lives of many Greeks and Romans, tells how the Roman armies under the command of Mark Anthony were poisoned by belladonna when they were searching for food during their retreat from the Parthians.

"They who sought for herbs," he says, "obtained few they had been accustomed to eat, and in tasting unknown herbs, they found one which occasioned madness and death."

Later on this same plant made it possible for Macbeth, King of Scotland, to win a victory. Pretending a truce, he sent bread and drinks of wine and ale mixed with belladonna leaves to the enemy troops, who were then easily massacred.

Every part of this plant is poisonous. It makes the temperature rise; the skin becomes hot, dry, and flushed; it blurs the vision; and causes hallucinations. Because of these symptoms produced by belladonna, it is said to make a person "hot as a hare, blind as a bat, dry as a bone, red as a beet, and mad as a hen." Its name, *belladonna,* comes from two Italian words: *bella,* meaning beautiful; and *donna,* meaning lady. Italian ladies were known to place a drop of its juice in their eyes to give them sparkle and to enlarge their pupils. They did not seem to mind the accompanying blurring of vision.

Through the ages people searched for ways of combating the effects of poisonous plants. Mithridates the Great, a king in Asia Minor about 100 B.C., is famous for his study of poisons. He tried out small doses of many poisonous plants on himself, and worked out a complicated formula of about fifty ingredients which would protect a man from any poison. One story tells that when he was defeated in battle by the Romans he tried suicide; but no poison would kill him because he had made himself immune with his own compound. This compound became known as Mithridatium and was regarded later

Mithridates

as the great antidote of Roman pharmacy. Changes were made in its ingredients, but the basic formula was used for more than a thousand years.

Emperors, kings, and men of high position had need of antidotes, for history is full of tales of the efforts made to poison them. Mushrooms were a favorite means, because they could be prepared in tasty dishes and go unnoticed.

There are about five thousand species of mushrooms, most of them harmless. There are some deadly ones, however, especially in the Amanita group. Two species of this group cause most of the deaths from mushroom eating. One of these is called the Death Cup or Destroying Angel, because its poison is so powerful. No amount of cooking removes the poison and there is no good antidote to counteract it. This deadly Amanita is a beautiful mushroom that grows in woods or along the edges of woods. Its poison attacks the liver and the kidneys and is usually fatal.

The other very poisonous Amanita is called the Fly Agaric. It received this name because before sticky flypaper came along, a brew of this poison mushroom was used to kill flies.

It is easily recognized by its bright scarlet cap spotted with white. Its poison affects the nervous system and brain and produces strange visions. Tribes of northeast Siberia ate them in small amounts to produce the excitement of these visions.

There are many other mildly poisonous mushrooms. For mushroom pickers the rule is to leave a mushroom alone unless you know beyond any doubt that it is edible.

Mushrooms belong to the plant group known as fungi. This group also includes mildews, molds, and other fungi that grow as parasites on higher plants.

Ergot is one of these parasitic fungi. It grows on rye plants and other grasses and produces black club-shaped lumps on the grains. It contains a virulent poison. In the tenth, eleventh, and twelfth centuries, it caused frightful epidemics in Europe.

Deadly Amanitas

Rye Ergot

Nobody knew then that the disease was due to the infected rye the people were using to make bread. Over 40,000 people died from ergot poisoning in one epidemic. Finally, in 1597, this fungus began to be suspect. By 1630 there was more evidence and by the end of the eighteenth century the ergot fungus was definitely known to be the cause.

Some plant poisons have been used for centuries by primitive people. In Africa, poison plants were used in a practice known as ordeal by poison. Among primitive tribes, a crop failure or an epidemic was thought to be due to the evil doings of a witch. The medicine men of the tribe decided who it was that they suspected, and forced that person to drink a dose of poison. If he or she survived, it was evidence of innocence. On the other hand, death meant guilt!

The chief use of poison plants among primitive people, however, was to poison their arrows and spears and blow darts. In Africa, the seeds of the woody Strophanthus vines went into the making of arrow poison. In South America, jungle Indians brewed the roots and barks from a number of plants into a sticky gum called curare.

For years, the plants that went into curare remained a mystery, because tribal priests guarded their secret carefully. Explorers brought back tall tales about its preparation. According to one story, certain old women skilled in the art were shut in at specified times and furnished with the materials. For two days these women watched and distilled the gum. As soon as it was finished, the house was opened. If the women were obviously well, instead of lying on the ground half dead from the fumes, they were punished and their brew was thrown away. For it was said, "The strength of the poison is such that the mere odor kills its maker." Other stories maintained that the preparers of the brew had to fall dead before the concoction was finished. These stories were fascinating, but untrue. We know today that the curare fumes are not poisonous, that curare can be eaten without ill effect, and that the poison must be introduced into the blood stream to be fatal. In the blood stream the poison paralyzes the muscles, including those controlling the heart and lungs.

It took a few hundred years to discover these things, and the kinds of plants that went into the brew. In the sixteenth century Sir Walter Raleigh, among others, wrote about curare. It was not until the nineteenth century, however, that Alexander von Humboldt watched the preparation of the poison. Samples of the plants used were sent to Europe, but they seemed to vary greatly with the locality of the tribe being observed. Meanwhile, efforts were being made in chemical laboratories to isolate the pure chemicals in this arrow poison. Then, in 1844, Claude Bernard, the famous French physiologist, showed that curare paralyzed the nerves that controlled muscles.

In the twentieth century medical men really became interested in curare and the effects it produced, but it was difficult to get enough material to experiment with. Again botanical explorers went to South America, lived and traveled among the Indians, and finally were able to supply good-sized amounts of curare to medical laboratories. They carefully collected the plants that were used, and noted how the Indians steeped them in water and then boiled them down to a gum-

Curare

my paste. They identified the plants that went into the brew. Today most curare is obtained from only one of these many plants—a tropical climber known as Chondodendron.

Curare is a valuable medicine when used in minute quantities. It was introduced in the 1930's to relax the muscles in operations on the stomach and intestines. It is used today to relax the muscles of polio victims who are being helped to regain the use of their limbs. It is also used to relax the muscles of people suffering from lockjaw.

Curare is like other plant poisons used as remedies. Taken in large doses it is deadly, but in small doses it is a useful medicine. This is true of most of the plant poisons mentioned so far. Small doses of aconite are used in liniments for neuralgia, and as a sedative for the heart. Strychnine in small doses stimulates the nervous system and the heart. The active chemicals in henbane have a quieting action on the nervous system. Poison hemlock contains a chemical that relaxes spasms and convulsions. Belladonna in small doses relaxes the spasms in nervous stomachs. Atropine, one of the chemicals extracted from belladonna, is used by eye specialists to dilate the pupil in eye examinations and to treat certain infections of the eyes. Belladonna also has in it the same chemical found in Jimson weed, which is valuable in the treatment of bomb shock, airsickness and seasickness. Ergot is used to control hemorrhage.

Even some of our lovely garden plants may be used as medicines in small doses, although they contain poisons. The lily of the valley, larkspur, English ivy, and several kinds of Narcissus are beautiful to look at, but dangerous to eat. Even shoots of the common potato and leaves of rhubarb are poisonous. In general, it is a good idea to be careful about tasting unfamiliar roots, stems, leaves, and bark.

CHAPTER 6

New Riches from Old Plants

PLANTS were used to cure disease in ancient days, but a whole new approach developed when it was found in the nineteenth century that microbes cause disease. One group of microbes, the bacteria, were shown to be tiny microscopic plants that cause diphtheria, pneumonia, tuberculosis, and many other diseases common to man. Louis Pasteur, the great French scientist, contributed much to this germ theory of disease. But he also contributed another important idea: that disease germs themselves might be killed—by other plant microbes, found in the soil. He noted that when people who had died of germ diseases were buried in the ground, the dangerous germs that went with them lasted only a few hours. He also noted that when air-borne bacteria fell upon a culture of the germ that caused anthrax (a cattle disease), the disease germs were destroyed. He decided that a microbe might possibly be made to fight another microbe!

For many years this idea interested various research workers. Observations here and there were made and recorded about how one species of microbe interfered with the growth of another microbe. In 1901 a germ-killing substance (pyocyanase) was isolated from a pus germ. But there were no real developments of this idea until one day in September, 1928.

On that day Alexander Fleming, a bacteriologist in St. Mary's Hospital in London, observed a strange thing on one of his dishes in which he was growing cultures of a disease germ. A blue-green mold had accidentally fallen on the culture, and around the mold there was a clear zone where the disease microbes were dissolving and disappearing! Evidently some product of the mold was passing out into the culture medium and destroying the germs. Dr. Fleming identified the mold as Penicillium, one of a large group of green molds found on cheese, fruit, and bread, and in the soil. He tried to extract the powerful chemical and finally managed to get a tiny quantity. He called it penicillin and proved that it could stop the growth of many common disease germs.

Because penicillin was so difficult to extract from the mold, the study was dropped until 1939. At that time Drs. Howard Florey, Ernest Chain, and Norman Heatley at Oxford University took up the study of penicillin. They managed to extract enough penicillin to prove that it could work wonders on the infections of laboratory animals. They tried it on one human patient, a London policeman, who was dying of a blood infection. He made a remarkable recovery, but eventually died because the supply of penicillin ran out.

War conditions in England made it impossible to find ways to manufacture penicillin in large quantities. So the research team came to the United States, and here, in co-operation with American scientists and production engineers, they worked out ways to produce penicillin on a mass scale. With the new methods, tons of penicillin were produced and used to save the lives of men suffering from infected wounds incurred in World War II. It became widely used in the treatment of serious bacterial infections such as pneumonia, meningitis, and scarlet fever. This common mold was found capable of producing a substance which destroyed these dangerous microbes. Here was the first practical antibiotic, or substance produced by one plant microbe that could prevent the growth of another microbe.

Scientists now set out to find new microbes that could produce antibiotics. A global search started. Thousands of soil samples were taken from the earth of forests, fields, and mountains all over the world and tested for molds or bacteria that could produce germ-killing substances. A most amazing group of antibiotics was found to be produced by different forms of a soil mold, Streptomyces. In 1944 research workers at Rutgers University isolated streptomycin from one such mold. It was found effective against many forms of bacteria that were resistant to penicillin. In a soil sample taken from a field near Caracas, Venezuela, another Streptomyces mold was found that secreted chloromycetin. Clinical tests of this new antibiotic showed that it was effective against typhus fever, typhoid, viral pneumonia, and whooping cough.

Aureomycin was isolated in 1948, from a species of Streptomyces found in a soil sample collected from a timothy field in Missouri. *Aureo* comes from a Latin word meaning gold. It was used in the name to describe the golden-yellow threads of the mold and the golden-yellow liquid it secretes. Aureomycin is used for a great many of the diseases that Chloromycetin reaches.

Terramycin was made available in the spring of 1950. It, too, comes from a species of Streptomyces. Striking cures have been made with this new antibiotic, which has been found to be effective against almost one hundred diseases. It is called a "broad-spectrum" antibiotic, because it can be used to stop the growth of so many different kinds of microbes.

Thousands of molds have been investigated. From these,

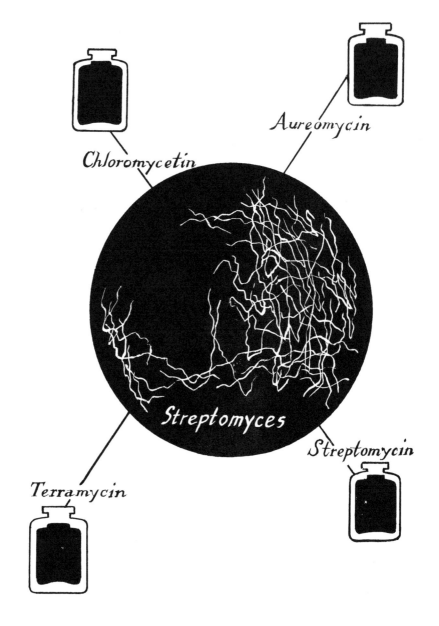

Chloromycetin

Aureomycin

Streptomyces

Terramycin

Streptomycin

more than three hundred antibiotics have been isolated. But only a few of these have moved from the laboratory to the drugstore.

Molds have no monopoly on antibiotic production in the plant kingdom. Bacteria have also yielded antibiotics. A common soil bacterium provided eleven different antibiotic substances. Most of the germ killers extracted from bacteria have been found to be poisonous when taken internally, but they have limited use as external salves. Although the term *antibiotic* was first used only in connection with substances produced by microbes, it has now been extended to similar substances recently found in more complex plants.

Three thousand different flowering plants were tested for their antibiotic activity against cultures of bacteria. The extracts of thirty different plant families were found to be effective! Buttercup juice stopped the growth of many disease germs, but it was found to be too poisonous for human use. Garlic, burdock, wild ginger, olives, dates, figs, onions, lettuce, celery, parsley, asparagus, horse-radish, peppers, cabbage, cloves, tomatoes, sweet potatoes, nasturtium, and honeysuckle were all found to have juices that killed common germs. As yet none of these have been tested enough to be used commercially.

In spite of the great advances made in the field of antibiotics, we have yet to find antibiotics for influenza, common colds, polio, measles, chicken pox, mumps, etc. We still need antibiotics to control fungus infections in man. And we still need some that will control plant diseases that wipe out great percentages of our food crops every year.

Vitamins from Plants

The great discoveries showing that microbes cause disease made it hard to find out that there were other diseases, caused by deficiencies in the diet. During the first quarter of the twentieth century it became known that there are diseases that can be caused by the lack of certain substances occurring in very minute quantities in our foods—the vitamins.

Actually, one vitamin disease had been known and treated a long time ago. Back in 1536 the Iroquois Indians in the neighborhood of present-day Quebec saved the lives of the crew accompanying the explorer, Jacques Cartier, by curing them of scurvy. No one knew then what caused the disease, but the Iroquois had a miraculous cure for it—an infusion of the bark and leaves of an evergreen tree. In 1720 a surgeon in the Austrian army observed that soldiers suffering from scurvy were cured by fresh vegetables. In 1747 Dr. James Lind learned that lemon or lime juice was a specific cure for scurvy. By 1804 a regular ration of lemon juice was given to the sailors in the

British navy. It wasn't until this century that we came to understand that scurvy is caused by the lack of Vitamin C, or ascorbic acid, which occurs naturally in plants.

At the turn of this century the Dutch were looking for ways to cure beriberi, a disease that was destroying their armies in Sumatra and seemed, mysteriously, to attack many people in the Far East. A young Dutch physician, Dr. Eijkman, set to work in a military hospital in Java to look for the cause of this disease. He kept looking for a microbe but could find none. By accident, the chickens he was using as experimental animals did not get their regular feed, and were fed on leftover white rice. In a short time they developed a peculiar disease that resembled beriberi. When the diet was changed to the regular unpolished rice with the brown husks left on, the chickens got well. After further research, it was found that beriberi was due to the lack of some substance present in the outer layer of the rice kernel. In 1912 the pure crystals of Vitamin B were extracted from the rice polishings.

Later on, Vitamin B was found to be a meaningless term, because it is a complex of many substances, B_1, B_2, B_3, etc. The various B vitamins occur in vegetables (both fresh and dried) and in meat, especially liver. They control nervous functions, and diseases such as pellagra and anemia.

Vitamin A, which cures night blindness, was found in butter fat and in yellow vegetables like carrots and sweet potatoes. Vitamin D, which cures rickets, was found in cod-liver oil, vitamin E in wheat-germ oil, and vitamin K in alfalfa.

Today vitamin production no longer wholly depends on the original sources in fruits, vegetables, rice polishings, etc., because most of the vitamins are being produced synthetically from simple chemicals. But nutrition is another field where plants helped man in his battle against disease.

More Plant Treasures

The search continues throughout the plant kingdom for more plants with healing powers. Every day the newspapers report new plant drug discoveries. New antibiotics come to the fore. A chemical from oatmeal is found to relieve ulcer pains. Papain, from the tropical papaya plant, heals infected wounds. A new vitamin in cabbage gives hope of an ulcer cure. Asparagus is found to strengthen capillaries. Licorice root has chemicals that have a hormone-like effect. The May apple has chemicals that destroy cancerous tumors in mice. All these things are just headlines today; but in the near future they may be proved, by long hard experimental work, to be of the greatest value to man.

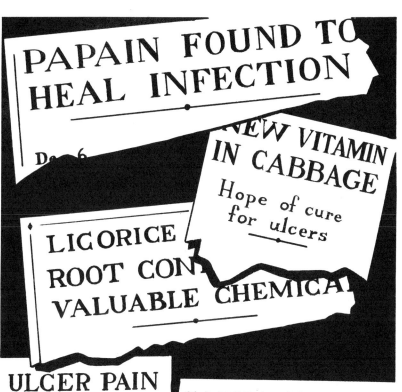

Scientific Names of Plants

Common names vary, but scientific names are recognizable
all over the world.

Common name	Scientific name
Aloe	different species of *Aloe*
Asparagus	*Asparagus officinalis*
Belladonna	*Atropa belladonna*
Blue cohosh	*Caulophyllum thalictroides*
Calamus root	*Acorus calamus*
Cascara	*Rhamnus purshiana*
Castor bean	*Ricinus communis*
Chaulmoogra	different species of *Hydnocarpus* and *Taraktogenos kurzii*
Chinese rhubarb	different species of *Rheum*
Cinchona	different species of *Cinchona*
Coca	*Erythroxylon coca*
Cocillan bark	*Guarea rusbyi*
Deadly nightshade	*Atropa belladonna*
Death cup Destroying angel	*Amanita phalloides*
English ivy	*Hedera helix*
Ephedra	different species of *Ephedra*
Ergot	*Claviceps purpurea*
Eucalyptus	different species of *Eucalyptus*
Fly agaric	*Amanita muscaria*
Foxglove	*Digitalis purpurea*
Ginseng	different species of *Panax*
Henbane	*Hyoscyamus niger*
Indian tobacco	*Lobelia inflata*
Ipecac	*Cephaëlis ipecacuanha*

93

Jimson weed	*Datura stramonium*
Larkspur	*Delphinium ajacis*
Licorice root	*Glycyrrhiza glabra*
Lily of the valley	*Convallaria majalis*
Lobelia	*Lobelia inflata*
Ma huang	different species of *Ephedra*
Mandrake	*Mandragora officinarum*
May apple	*Podophyllum peltatum*
Mexican yam	different species of *Dioscorea*
Monkshood	*Aconitum napellus*
Narcissus	different species of *narcissus*
Oleander	*Nerium oleander*
Opium poppy	*Papaver somniferum*
Papaya	*Carica papaya*
Poison hemlock	*Conium maculatum*
Poison nut tree	*Strychnos nux vomica*
Psyllium	different species of *Plantago*
Sarsaparilla	different species of *Smilax*
Sassafras	*Sassafras variifolium*
Senna	different species of *Cassia*
Snakeroot plant	*Rauwolfia serpentina*
Squill	different species of *Urginea*
Strophanthus	different species of *Strophanthus*
Sweet flag	*Acorus calamus*
Thorn apple	*Datura stramonium*
White water lily	*Nymphaea alba*
Willow	different species of *Salix*
Wintergreen	*Gaultheria procumbens*

INDEX

(* indicates illustrations)

I N D E X — *Continued*

(* indicates illustrations)